IS IT SO?

Designed by Chestnut House/Dick Martin

Illustrated by
K. Y. Craft
Pat Maloney
Andrew Epstein
Dick Martin

Structural Reading Program

IS IT SO?

Toni Gould
Kathleen Teague

🏠 **RANDOM HOUSE School Division**

Toni S. Gould is most grateful to Lynn McVeigh
for contributing her imaginative ideas and
creativity to some of the stories created in
this reader.

Contents

A PET FOR TIM

"I wish I had a pet," said Tim.

"Jeff has a pup.
Peg has a cat.
Dick has fish.
But I have no pet."

Is this a pet for Tim?

Can it nap on his bed?

Is this a pet for Tim?

Can it sit with him?

8

Is this a pet for Tim?

Can it run and hop with him?

9

Is this a pet for Tim?

Yes, it is.
It can sit with him.
It can run with him.
It is fun to have a pup
for a pet.

10

A FAT CAT

Tom is a sad cat.
Tom is big and fat.

"I will run and run,"
said Tom.

"That is what I will do.
Then I will get thin!"

That is what Tom did.

Tom ran and ran.

Tom ran to the top of a hill.

Tom met a fox on the top of the hill.

"Tell me, Fox," said Tom.
"I ran and ran.
Did I get thin?"

"No!" said the fox.
"You are big and fat."

Tom ran on and on.
Tom was mad at the fox.

Then Tom met a duck.
"Tell me, Duck," said Tom.
"I ran and ran.
Am I thin?"

"No!" said the duck.
"You are big and fat."

Tom got mad at the duck
and ran on.

Then Tom met a hen.
Tom sat with the hen
to have a chat.

"Tell me, Hen," said Tom.
"I ran and ran, but I did
not get thin. What can I do?"

"Do not be sad,"
said the hen.

It is not bad to be big
and fat.

Thin cats eat and eat
to get big and fat."

18

"What luck!" said Tom.
"I do not have to get fat.
I am big and fat.
I will run back and tell
the fox and the duck."

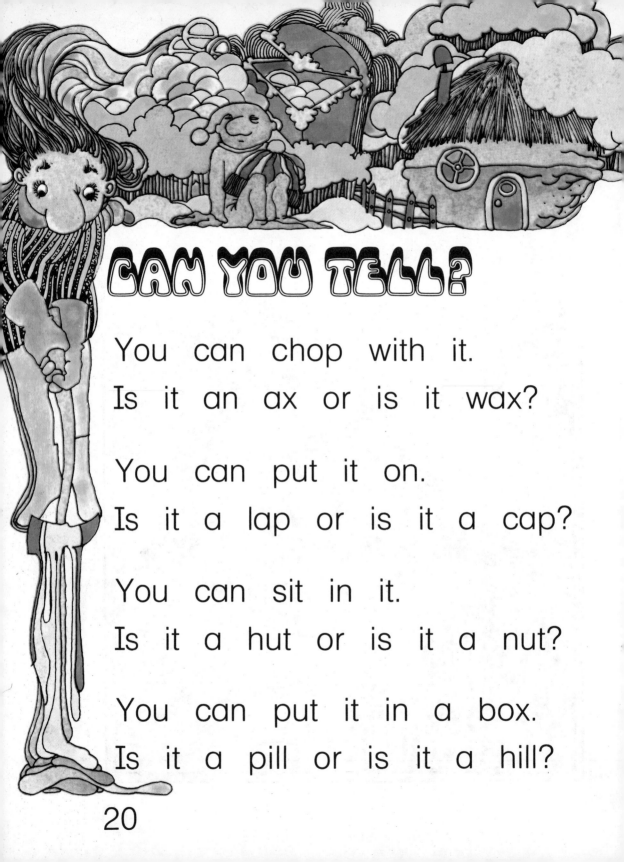

CAN YOU TELL?

You can chop with it.
Is it an ax or is it wax?

You can put it on.
Is it a lap or is it a cap?

You can sit in it.
Is it a hut or is it a nut?

You can put it in a box.
Is it a pill or is it a hill?

20

CAN YOU TELL?

You can put it on a bun.
Is it jam or is it Sam?

You can fill it.
Is it a fan or is it a pan?

You can pick it up.
Is it a bell or is it a well?

You can lock it.
Is it a fox or is it a box?

Nan and the Box

"Mom," said Nan.
"Who put that box
on the desk?
Is it for me?"

"I put it on the desk,"
said Mom.

"But it is not for you."

"Then it must be for Ken,"
said Nan.

"Will you send it to him
at camp?"

"No, Nan," said Mom.
"It is not for Ken."

"I will give it to Dad,"
said Nan.
"The box is on his desk.
It must be for him."

24

"No, Nan, it is not for Dad," said Mom.

"It is not for me," said Nan.

"And it is not for Ken or Dad.
It must be for you.
Tell me what it is."

"No, Nan," said Mom.
"It is not for me."

"I give up!" said Nan.
"Who is it for?"
Just then Rex ran
to the desk.

26

Up he went!
The box fell.

"It is for Rex!"
yells Nan.
"I did not think
of you!"

27

THE LITTLE LOST DUCK

Mother Duck and her little ducks went to the pond.

28

"I had six little ducks,"
said Mother Duck.

"I have lost a duck!

I must go back and look
for it."

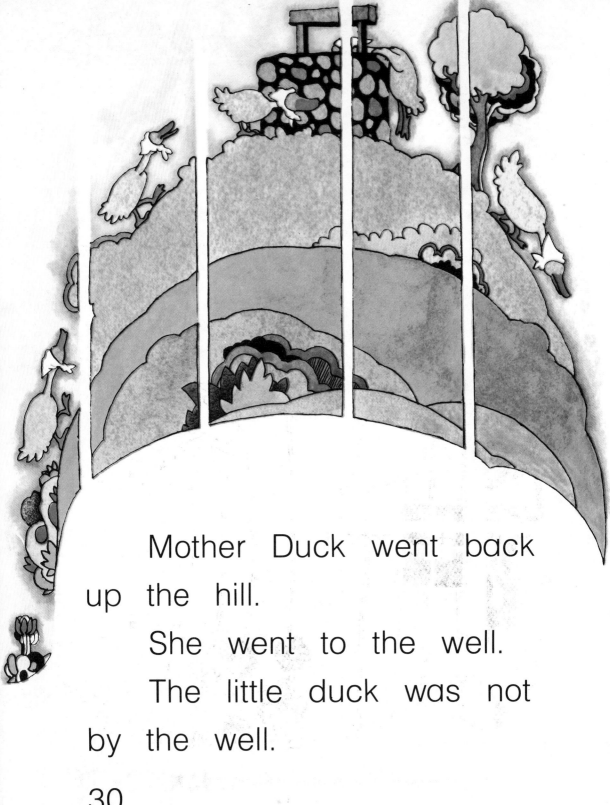

Mother Duck went back
up the hill.
She went to the well.
The little duck was not
by the well.

Next Mother Duck went to look in the shed.

But there was no little duck in the shed.

Then Mother Duck went
to look by the milk cans.
There was milk in the
cans, but no little duck.

Mother Duck met a hen
with her little chicks.

Mother Hen had ten chicks,
but no little duck.

At last Mother Duck was
back at the nest.

"Quack! Quack!"

Little Duck was in the nest!

34

"Quack! Quack! Quack!"
said Mother Duck.
"There you are.
You are not lost.
You did not wish to go
to the pond with us."

Can It Be?

Jill went to get the dust mop for her mom.

But the mop ran and sat next to the lamp.

36

Can It Be?

Lee must have a pad and pen.

Mom put them on her list.

The list will run to the shop, and get the pad and pen.

THAT DOG

Jeff has to get up.
He gets out of bed and
looks for his socks.

Mom is up.
She looks for her .
Dad is up, too.
He looks for his .

"Where is that dog?"
yells Dad.
  "Jeff, look for Jip!"

In runs Jeff.

"Just look at that!"
said Dad.
"Where is that dog?"

Jeff runs back to Dad.
Jip is with him.

"Look at that," yells Dad.
"Give it to me.
You are a bad dog."

"I have to get to my job,"
said Dad.
"Where is my hat?"

"You will be mad," said Jeff.
"Jip had it in his box.
This is what is left of it."

"Jip, you have had it,"
said Jeff.
"Dad is mad at you.
Get in that box."

Dad went out.

Mom and Jeff went to get the bus.

Jip sat in his box.
Jip was sad.
This was no fun.

So Jip went out, too!

FROGS, FROGS, FROGS!

Tom had lots of frogs.
He kept them in a tank.
But one day he did not
put the lid back on the tank.
That was a day!

One frog hid in Nan's crib.
When Nan got up from
her nap, there sat a frog!

One frog hid in the sink.
When Pam went to get a
glass, there sat a frog!

One frog hid on the top
of Mom's hat.

When Mom went to get it,
there sat a frog!

Mom was mad at Tom.

"Tom, get this frog,"
she said.

"Or I will get the mop."

Tom ran and got the frog that was on Mom's hat.

He ran and got the frog that was in Nan's crib.

He ran and got the frog that was in the sink.

Tom put the frogs back
in the tank.
All but one!

Dad went to fill the tub.
There was a frog in the tub.

Dad went to look for Tom.
Dad was mad, too.
That was bad for Tom.

At last Tom had all of
the frogs back in the tank.
From then on, he put the
lid on the tank.

A Gift for Jeff

"Tim," said Mom, "go and tell Dad that Jeff is sick.

I think he has the mumps.

He can not go with you and Dad."

"That is too bad," said Dad.
"Jeff will miss the fun.
But he can go with us
on the next trip."

Dad and Tim went to
Plum Pond to fish and swim.

"This is fun," said Tim.
"But I miss Jeff.
Too bad he got sick."

"It was too bad," said Dad.

"Run and look at what they sell at that stand. Pick out a gift for Jeff."

Tim ran back to Dad.

"They sell trucks,"
said Tim.

"Can I bring Jeff
a dump truck?"

"O.K.," said Dad.

"Get it and I will be
at the bus stop."

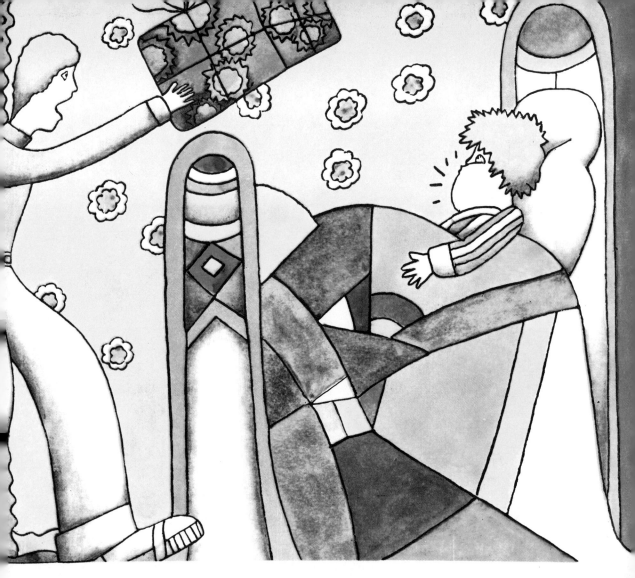

Tim ran to tell Jeff that
he went to Plum Pond.
"And this is for you,
Jeff," said Tim.

"For me!" said Jeff.

"Well, Jeff," said Mom.
"I do not think it is
so bad to be sick.
Do you?"

"No, not when you get
a dump truck," said Jeff
with a big grin.

IS IT SO? Yes or No?

Can a duck swing a bat?
Can a dog nap on a mat?

Can a girl sit very still?
Can a song run up the hill?

Can a hen mend Jill's socks?
Can a box jump on the rocks?

Can a clock stand at the sink?
Can a boy spill all this ink?

IS IT SO? Yes or No?

Can a frog put on a ring?
Can a boy get on a swing?

Can a fox fix Tom's sled?
Can the sun rest in bed?

Can a skunk ring this bell?
Can an ox get up and spell?

Can a doll be in a crib?
Can a clam have on a bib?

64

The Twins

Bob and Ken are twins.
Bob plays with Ken, and
Ken plays with Bob.

Ken is mad at Bob.
He runs to Mom.

"Mom," yells Ken.
"Look at what Bob did
to my drum."

"Bob," said Mom.
"What did you do to
Ken's drum?"

"I sat on it,"
said Bob.

"But Bob," said Mom,
"why did you do that?"

"Ken lost my truck,"
said Bob.

"That is why I sat
on his drum.

I am still mad at him."

"And I am still mad
at Bob," said Ken.

68

"Boys, stop it," said Mom.
"This is what we will do."

Mom and the boys went out.

At the shop, Mom said,
"Boys, you can have this.
Ken, you go and get a
truck for Bob."

"If I get him a truck,"
said Ken, "will Bob get
me a drum?"

"Yes, I will," said Bob.

"The twins get on so well," said Dad.

"Yes," said Mom.

The Witch and the Fox

"I think I will stop and have a nap," said the witch. "Then I will have lunch."

73

The witch put the lunch
bag on the grass.

Then she sat down to
nap.

A fox ran past the witch.

"I smell lunch," said the fox.

"It must be in that bag."

The fox ran up to the
witch, and ran off with the bag.
"Stop!" said the witch.
"Bring back my lunch."

But the fox did not stop.

The witch was mad.

"What a bad fox to run
off with my lunch," she said.
"I will fix him."

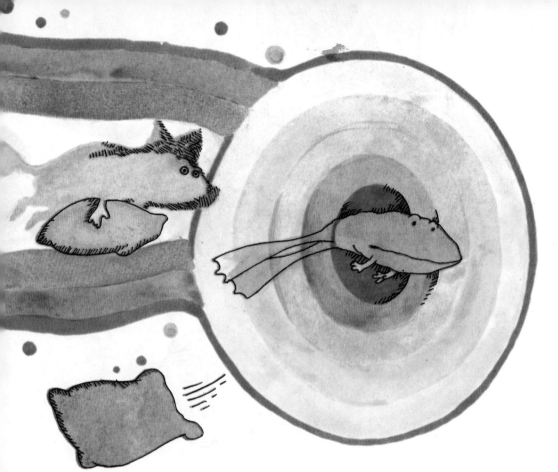

"You will not have my lunch," said the witch.

"I can stop you.

I will cast a spell on you."

And that is just what she did!

With the clap of her hands, the bad fox was a frog!

Off he ran, and left the bag of lunch on the grass.